Richard Scarry's
Great Big
Schoolhouse

First published in hardback by HarperCollins Publishers in 1977
This edition published by HarperCollins Children's Books in 2012

HarperCollins Children's Books is a division of HarperCollins Publishers Ltd,
77-85 Fulham Palace Road, London W6 8JB

1 3 5 7 9 10 8 6 4 2

ISBN: 978-0-00-793526-0

The HarperCollins website address is www.harpercollins.co.uk

Printed and bound in China.

Richard Scarry's
Great Big Schoolhouse

HarperCollins *Children's Books*

Getting Ready for School

Huckle's mother woke him up.
"It's time to get up for school," she said.
"Why do I have to go to school?" asked Huckle.
"All children go to school to learn how to read
and write," said his mother. "You want to be able
to read and write don't you? Now please get up."

Huckle got up. He yawned and rubbed the sleep
out of his eyes. He walked to the bathroom.

He washed his face
with soap and warm water.

He brushed his teeth.

He combed his hair
with cold water.

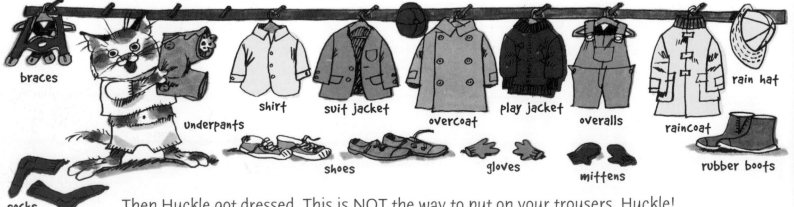

Then Huckle got dressed. This is NOT the way to put on your trousers, Huckle!

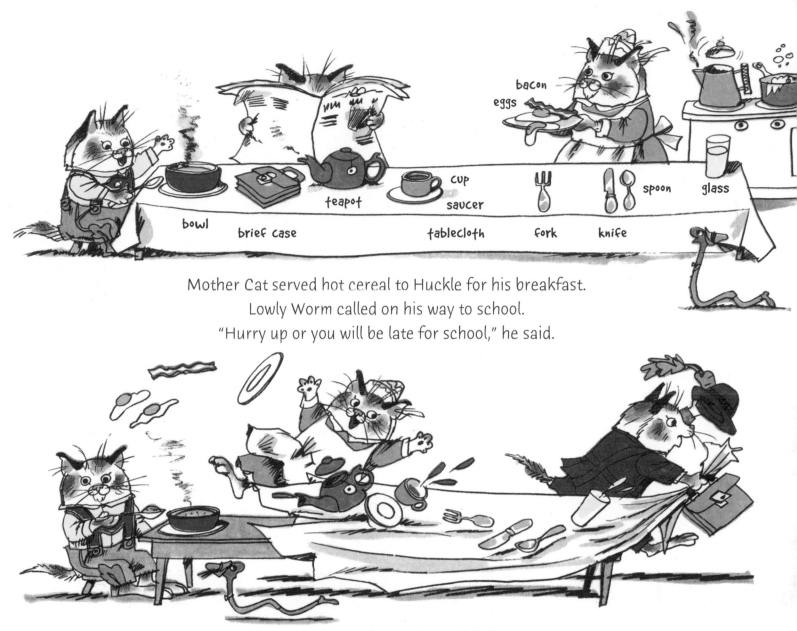

bacon
eggs

cup

saucer

spoon

glass

bowl   brief case   teapot   tablecloth   fork   knife

Mother Cat served hot cereal to Huckle for his breakfast.
Lowly Worm called on his way to school.
"Hurry up or you will be late for school," he said.

"LATE! My goodness! I am late for work," said Father Cat. He picked
up his briefcase and ran. Oh dear! He picked up the tablecloth, too!

Mother Cat walked with Huckle to the school bus stop.
Honk! Honk! The school bus came
to take the children to school.

SCHOOL

SCHOOL
BUS
STOP

SCHOOL BUS

Riding on the School Bus

black engine

red and green coach

Every day Huckle rides to school in his orange school bus.
He sees many colourful things. Everything has a colour.
What colour is the fisherman's suit?

purple jeep

SCHOOL BUS

manhole

street

red motorcycle

Gorilla Bananas and his yellow Bananamobile

orange aeroplane

white ambulance with red crosses

railway crossing gate

crossing guard

traffic light

blue sign

red fire engine

yellow crossing

GO RIGHT

fisherman

green taxi

tugboat

TAXI

brown delivery van

bridge

river

The School

This is Huckle's school. The school bus stopped at the school. The school bell rang. It was time for school to begin. But what was all that noise outside?

policeman

chimney sweep

school crossing guard

school library

classroom

classroom

classroom

classroom

classroom

doctor's office

Why, it was Joe, the caretaker!
As usual, he was late for school.

balloon

alphabet

Aa Aa | Bb Bb | Cc Cc | Dd Dd

string

clock

bell

wall

notice board

calendar

teacher

SEPTEMBER

SUN	MON	TUES	WED	THU	FRI	SAT
		1	2	3	4	5
6	7	8	9	10	11	12
13	14	15	16	17	18	19
20	21	22	23	24	25	26
27	28	29	30			

map

umbrella

overshoes

desk

pupils

The Classroom

This is Huckle's classroom. And behind the desk sits
Miss Honey, his teacher. Every morning the pupils say,
"Good morning, Miss Honey." And every morning, she says,
"Good morning, children. My, don't you look bright
and fresh this morning!" She always says that.

LEARNING THE ALPHABET

Aa Bb Cc Dd Ee Ff Gg Hh Ii Jj Kk Ll
Mm Nn Oo Pp Qq Rr Ss Tt Uu Vv Ww Xx Yy Zz

Each day Miss Honey teaches her class something new.
Today she was going to teach them the alphabet. She gave each child
a card with one of the letters of the alphabet on it. Everyone tried
to think of words that began with the letters on the cards.

yum yum!

A is the first letter of the **a**lphabet.
Arthur Pig brought **an a**pple for the teacher.
He **a**lso brought one for his friend, Lowly Worm.

apple

broom

bowl

book

bench

boot

"**B**ananas Gorilla! Take that **B**ananamobile **b**ack
outside where it **b**elongs!" said Miss Honey.
"And please eat your **b**reakfast at home!"

banana

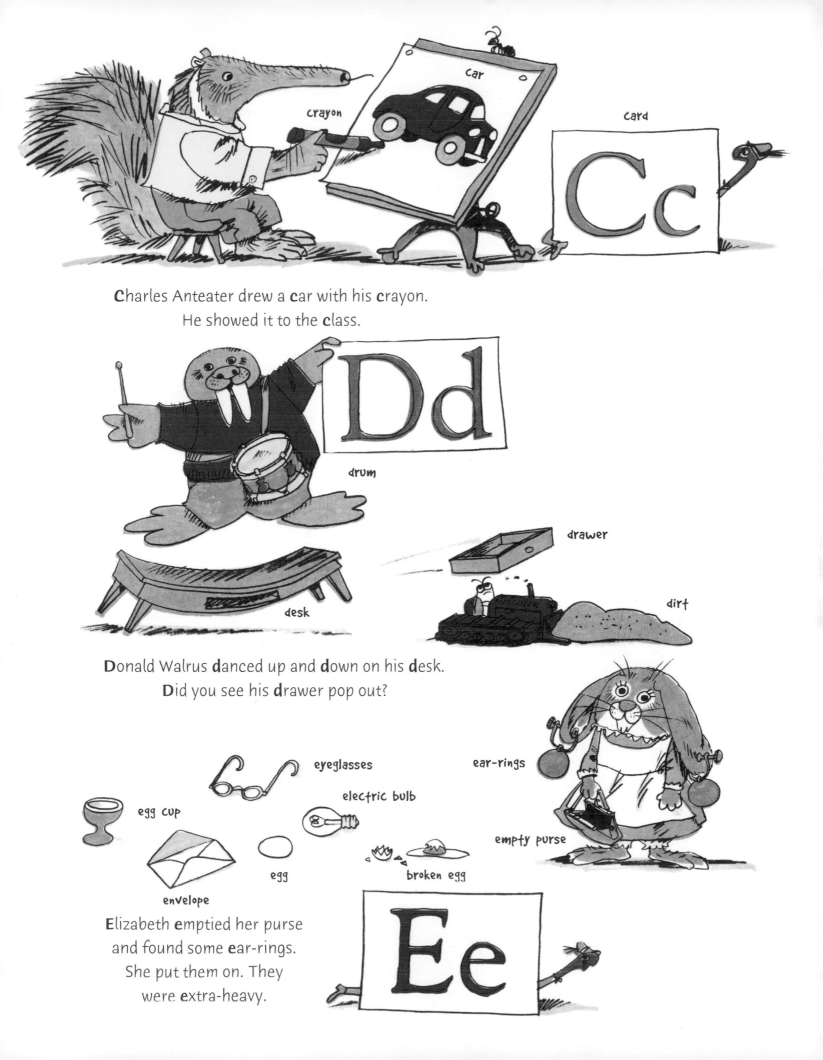

crayon

car

card

Cc

Charles Anteater drew a **c**ar with his **c**rayon.
He showed it to the **c**lass.

Dd

drum

desk

drawer

dirt

Donald Walrus **d**anced up and **d**own on his **d**esk.
Did you see his **d**rawer pop out?

eyeglasses

ear-rings

electric bulb

egg cup

empty purse

envelope

egg

broken egg

Elizabeth **e**mptied her purse
and found some **e**ar-rings.
She put them on. They
were **e**xtra-heavy.

Ee

Frances Raccoon showed the children her doll's
furniture. Lowly Worm turned on the bath tap
and pretended to be a fountain.

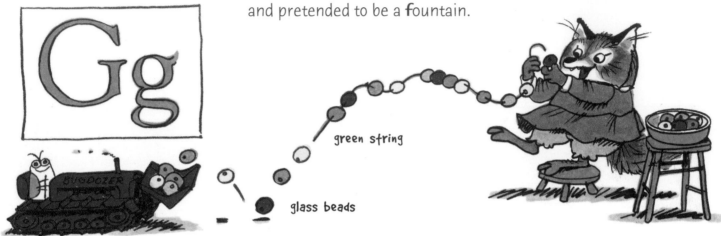

Gloria Fox strung glass beads on a green string.
She forgot that there are two ends to a piece
of string. Bugdozer gathered up the runaway beads.

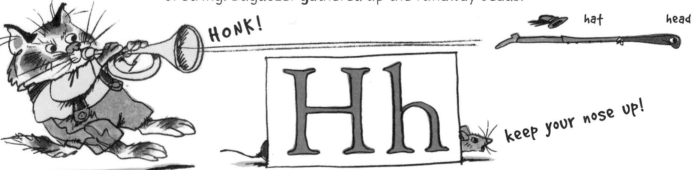

Huckle blew hard on his horn. Lowly was
hiding inside it. Now Lowly knows how to fly!

Irving Goat is playing
with Lowly.

jam

orange juice

Jj

Jimmy Crocodile spread orange juice
on his bread and poured jam in his glass.
Now just a minute! Isn't that wrong?

Kk

kerchief

how do you get it to come out?

ketchup

bread knife

sharp
kitchen
knives

kettle

Kathy is wearing a scarf. Lowly is shaking the
ketchup. Kathy is showing us things that are used
in the kitchen. Never touch sharp kitchen knives.

ladder

Ll

laundry

All right, Lowly! How many things can
you name that begin with the letter 'L'?

lemon

lamp

log

leaf

letter
to post

lantern

lettuce

loaf of
bread

lunch box

Very good, Lowly! Now, please take your seat.

melon

Mm

Mildred Hippo is a magician.
She can make things disappear.
She put a melon in her mouth.
She munched on it.
It disappeared! Mmmm! Good!
My! What a marvellous trick!

nut

nose (or trunk)

Ned's turn was next. He balanced
a nut on his nose. He wore
a napkin because he did
not want to get any crumbs
on his new suit.

napkin

Nn

new suit

Oo

orange

oil

onion

oboe

oak leaf

tin-opener

oar

Oliver Octopus has many objects to show. He often forgets to take
off his overcoat in the classroom. He played an old lullaby on his oboe.

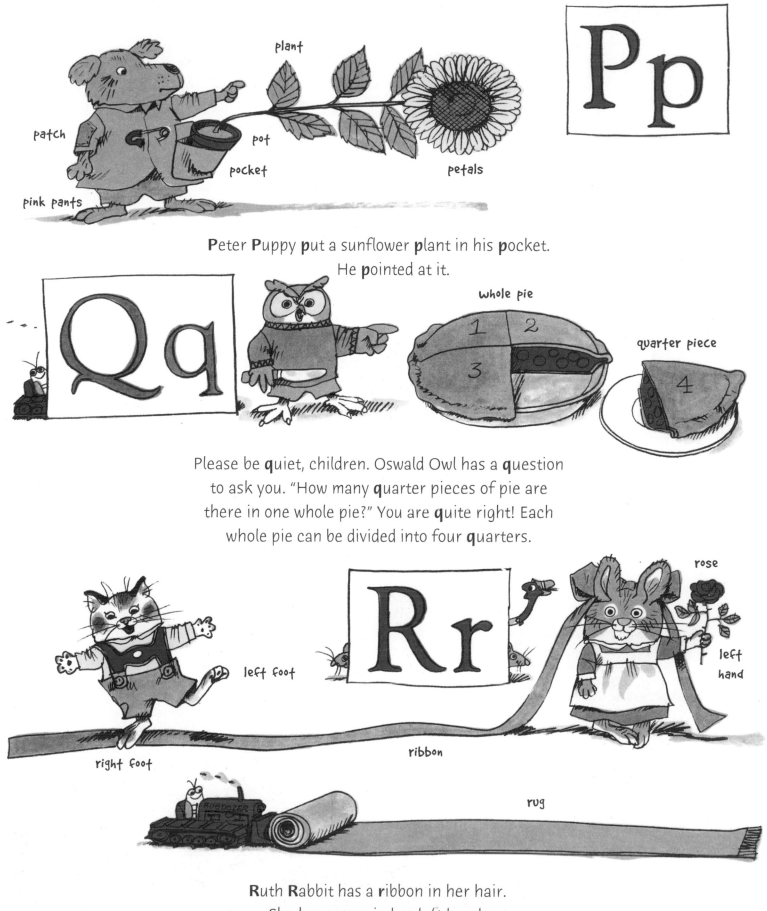

P p

plant

patch

pot

pocket

petals

pink pants

Peter Puppy put a sunflower plant in his pocket.
He pointed at it.

Q q

whole pie

1 2

3

quarter piece

4

Please be quiet, children. Oswald Owl has a question
to ask you. "How many quarter pieces of pie are
there in one whole pie?" You are quite right! Each
whole pie can be divided into four quarters.

R r

rose

left foot

left hand

right foot

ribbon

rug

Ruth Rabbit has a ribbon in her hair.
She has a rose in her left hand.
Huckle has a ribbon under his right foot.
Bugdozer is rolling up the rug.

Spotty Leopard **s**howed his **s**choolmates a tube of paste. He **s**queezed it.
It **s**quirted. It made a **s**pot. Paste is **s**ticky. Miss Honey told **S**potty
to get some **s**oap and water.

shirt

spot

tail

torn trousers

ball of twine

Tom Tiger **t**old everyone how to **t**ie a knot.
He **t**ook **t**wo pieces of **t**wine
and **t**ied them **t**ogether.

Ursula Pig stays **u**nder her
umbrella when it rains.
She has **u**sed it a lot.

vine

Victor Bear showed some pretty **v**iolets
and a **v**ine in a **v**ase. He tripped on the **v**ine.

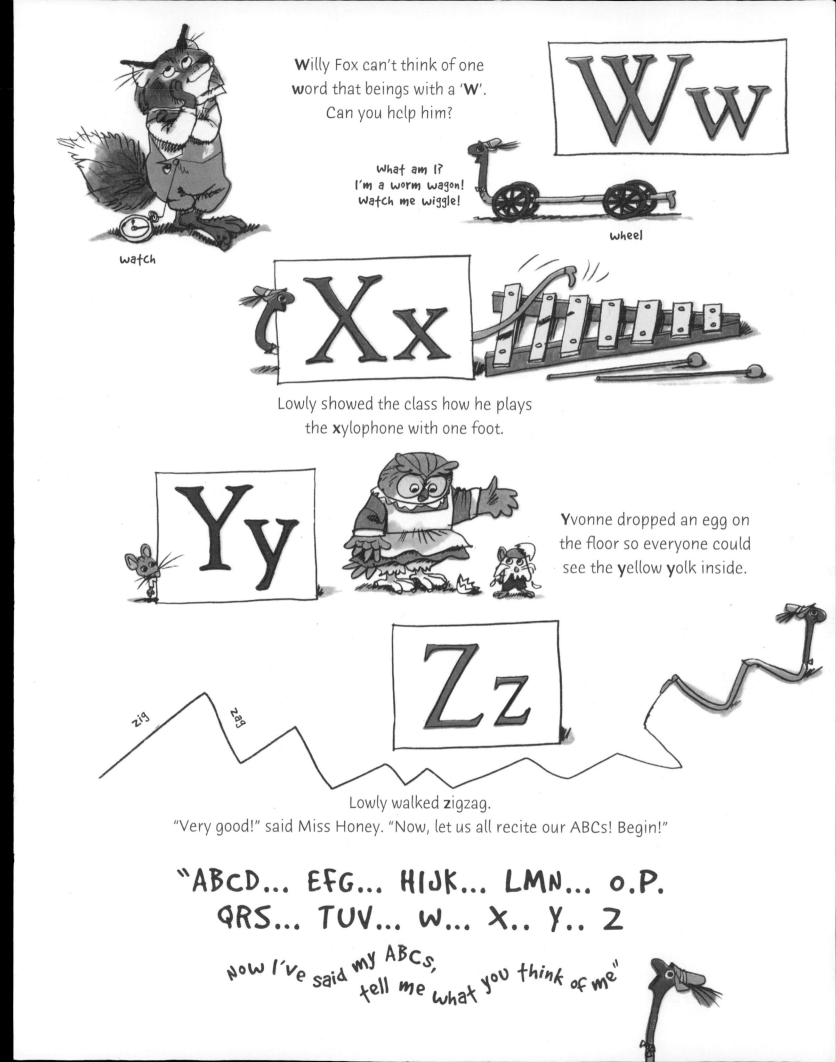

Willy Fox can't think of one
word that beings with a '**W**'.
Can you help him?

What am I?
I'm a **w**orm **w**agon!
Watch me **w**iggle!

wheel

watch

Lowly showed the class how he plays
the **x**ylophone with one foot.

Yvonne dropped an egg on
the floor so everyone could
see the **y**ellow **y**olk inside.

zig   zag

Lowly walked **z**igzag.
"Very good!" said Miss Honey. "Now, let us all recite our ABCs! Begin!"

"ABCD... EFG... HIJK... LMN... O.P.
QRS... TUV... W... X.. Y.. Z

Now I've said my ABCs,
tell me what you think of me"

Making Things

Miss Honey showed us how to make all kinds
of exciting things with a few simple
materials and tools.

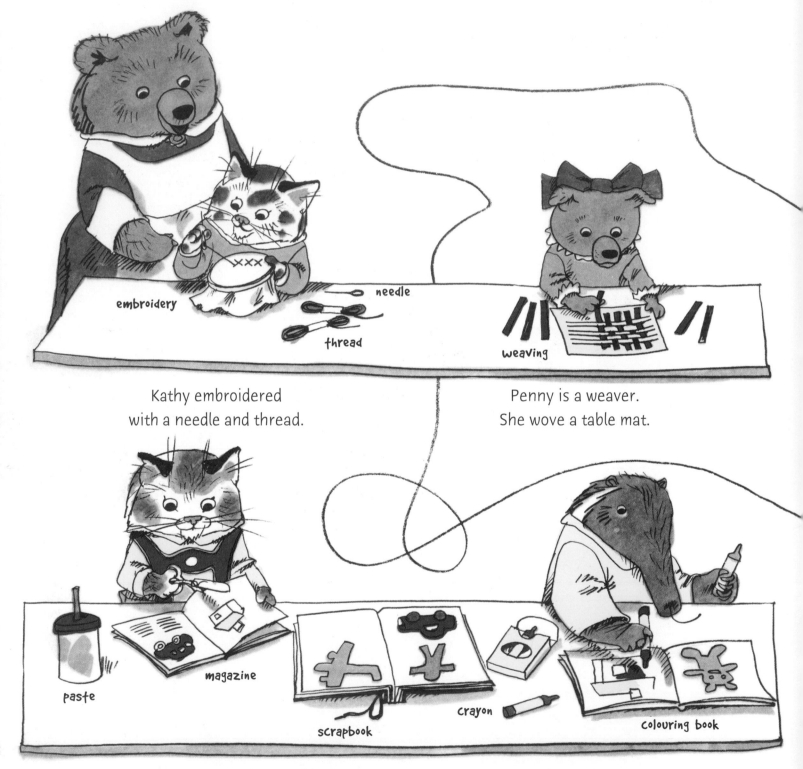

embroidery
needle
thread
weaving

paste
magazine
scrapbook
crayon
colouring book

Kathy embroidered
with a needle and thread.

Penny is a weaver.
She wove a table mat.

Huckle cut up pictures out of old
magazines and made a scrapbook.

Charlie coloured a colouring
book with crayons.

knitting bobbin

stringing beads

Frances knitted a pullover for Lowly.

Ruth strung beads on a string.

modelling clay

Willy modelled a bunny with modelling clay.

building blocks

Robert built a tower with building blocks.
Stop Robert! That is enough!

making things
with paper

paper aeroplanes

Mary cut out pieces of paper and
folded them up. She made a dolls' house.

Arthur folded paper, too. He made paper aeroplanes.
ARTHUR PIG! You know better than to throw things in class!

Playtime in the Playground

Every day the children have a short time for play.
When the weather is nice they play in the playground.

swing

rings

climbing ladder

sliding pole

shovel

bucket

sand box

barrel

hurt knee

hide and seek

kicking a ball

ring-a-ring-a-rosie

marbles

jacks

see-saw

slide

ring toss

leap frog

catching a ball

tag

skipping rope

pat-a-cake

hop scotch

stilts

The Days of the Week

Sunday Monday Tuesday Wednesday Thursday Friday Saturday

At school, Miss Honey teaches us many things.
When she is not teaching, she is very busy doing other things.

On **Sunday** afternoon, she drove out into the country with her friend
Mr Bruno to have a picnic. Picnics are always fun. Don't you think so?

On **Monday** after school, she did her washing.

On **Tuesday** morning before school, she baked
a cake for the sick children in the hospital.

Mother Cat took it to them.

On **Wednesday** she made up packages of used clothing to send to children who do not have enough to wear.

On **Thursday** she met the head and the other teachers to plan a school picnic.

On **Friday** she went to the library to read books and study. She is always learning new things to teach the children.

On **Saturday** she did her shopping. And on Saturday night she invited Mr Bruno to supper. He always brings flowers when he visits her.

You are a very busy lady, Miss Honey!

LEARNING TO COUNT

0 zero 1 one 2 two 3 three 4 four 5 five
6 six 7 seven 8 eight 9 nine 10 ten

zero

stool

"Now we shall learn how to count," said Miss Honey.
"Huckle will hold the card showing the correct answer.
How many children are sitting on the stool?" she asked.
The answer is **none**. There is no one sitting there.
We use the figure **zero** to show **none**.

flower

1 one

vase

How many flowers are in the vase on
Miss Honey's desk? You are right, Huckle.
There is just **one** flower.

2 two

When those little girls stop talking,
how many quiet little girls will there be?
There will be **two** quiet little girls
when they stop talking.

Roger Raccoon drew a picture of the teacher,
a picture of Huckle, and a picture of Lowly.
If you say he drew **three** pictures, you are right!

Arthur Pig had some big marbles in his pocket.
His pocket ripped open and they fell out.
One, two, three, **four**. **Four** bouncing marbles.

Miss Honey asked Willy Fox to take the wastepaper baskets out and
empty them. But, Willy don't take them all out at once! Empty the
five wastepaper baskets one at a time! One, two, three, four, **five**.

Well, what a mess Willy made! How many
brooms did the class use to clean it up?
Six brooms is the right answer.

Now, why are all those children raising their hands? It's because they want to ask Miss Honey
for permission to go to the cloakroom. You always have to ask, you know. "All right, you may go.
But hurry back," said the teacher. **Seven** children left the room to go to the lavatory.

Miss Honey asked Oliver to wipe the chalk off the blackboard with the dusters.
How many dusters did he use? He has **eight** arms so he used **eight** dusters.

By the time the blackboard was wiped
clean, the dusters were full of chalk dust.
Miss Honey asked some children to clap the dusters
to clean them. How many are clapping dusters?

one two three four five six seven eight nine

Huckle can count **nine** children.

Miss Honey asked Bananas Gorilla
what he brought to school to eat at
playtime. Did he bring **ten** bananas?
No! He brought **ten** bunches of bananas!

one two three four five

six seven eight nine ten

My! He does like bananas! Now let us all count from **one** to **ten**.
One, two, three, four, five, six, seven, eight, nine, ten.
Very good, children!

The Hours of the Day

It was Saturday. There was no school.
But there were lots of things for Huckle to do.
His friend Lowly was coming to spend the day
with him. He was going to stay overnight, too.

At **7** o'clock Huckle bounced out of bed.

At **8** o'clock he ate his breakfast. Father Cat
took the tablecloth to work with him again.

At **9** o'clock he tidied his room.

At **10** o'clock he went shopping for food.

At **11** o'clock he played in his muddy yard with Lowly. He fell down a few times.

12 o'clock is noontime, Huckle and Lowly ate their lunches. Lowly remembered to take his hat off at the table.

At **1** o'clock they both lay down and had a nap.

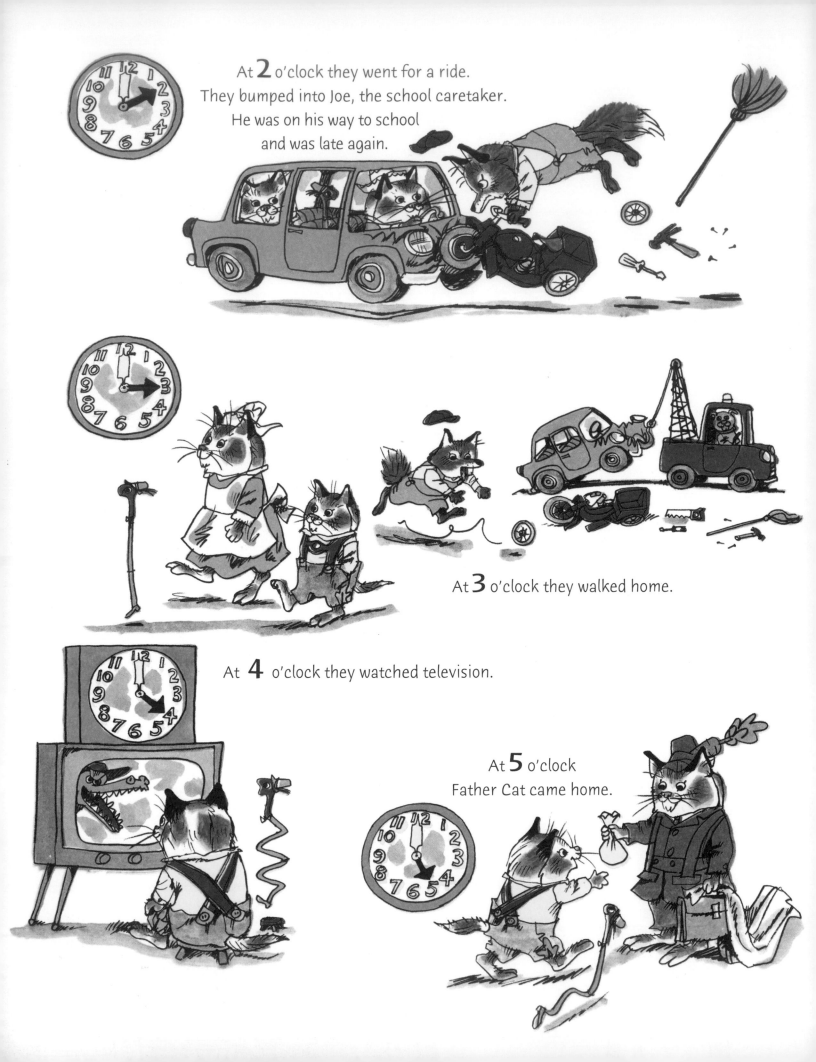

At **2** o'clock they went for a ride.
They bumped into Joe, the school caretaker.
He was on his way to school
and was late again.

At **3** o'clock they walked home.

At **4** o'clock they watched television.

At **5** o'clock
Father Cat came home.

At **6** o'clock Mother Cat served a surprise for supper. She served Huckle's guest first.

At **7** o'clock Father Cat gave Huckle and Lowly their baths. "Where did that soap go?" asked Father Cat.

At **8** o'clock Father Cat read them a bedtime story in bed.

And at **9** o'clock they were sound asleep. Sleep tight, Huckle! Sleep tight, Lowly!

Miss Honey's Busy Helpers

Everyone helps in little ways to make Miss Honey's life happier.
Miss Honey will never forget the day when Lowly polished her apple.

That same day Roger opened the window
and the papers blew away.

Arthur closed the door so that
they wouldn't escape.

Miss Honey remembers that Huckle
sharpened the pencils that day.
He made them a little too short.

Patsy picked up
papers off the floor and put
them in the wastepaper basket.

Eddie cleaned
the blackboard.

Peter washed the
blackboard with a sponge.

Bobby clapped the dusters.
Miss Honey was about to tell him
to clean them outside when...

...she saw that someone was watering her plant!

"STOP IT!" she cried.

Why, it was another of her busy helpers!
Joe the caretaker! He had been washing
the outside of the windows.
"Did you get a little wet?" he asked.
"You forgot to tell someone
to close the window!"
OH, JOE! You should have looked!

Measuring Things

"Now we shall learn something about how to measure things," said Miss Honey.

I use a ruler to measure my height.
I am **taller** than Bugdozer.
He is **shorter** than I am.

ruler

I use a scale to measure my weight.
I weigh **more** than Lowly.
He weighs **less** than I do.
I am **heavier** than he is.
He is **lighter** than I am.

scales

My arm is **longer** than Mouse's.
His arm is **shorter** than mine.

A clock measures time.
I woke **before** the sun came up.

Huckle woke **after** the sun came up.
I have been awake a **longer** time than Huckle.
He has been awake a **shorter** time than I have.

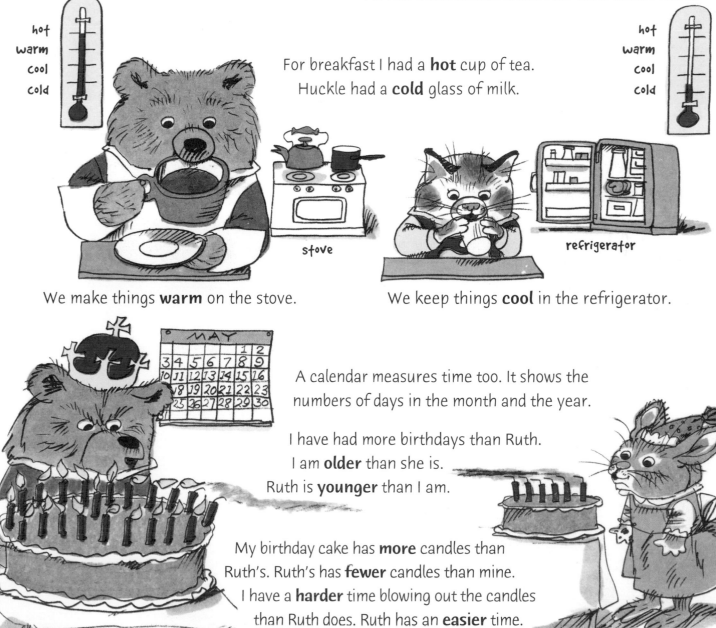

hot
warm
cool
cold

For breakfast I had a **hot** cup of tea.
Huckle had a **cold** glass of milk.

hot
warm
cool
cold

stove

refrigerator

We make things **warm** on the stove.

We keep things **cool** in the refrigerator.

A calendar measures time too. It shows the
numbers of days in the month and the year.

I have had more birthdays than Ruth.
I am **older** than she is.
Ruth is **younger** than I am.

My birthday cake has **more** candles than
Ruth's. Ruth's has **fewer** candles than mine.
I have a **harder** time blowing out the candles
than Ruth does. Ruth has an **easier** time.

Shapes

"Everything has a shape," said Miss Honey.
"I will show you different kinds of shapes.
First, look at my shape. Mr Bruno says I have
a beautiful shape. Would you say that I am
fatter or **thinner** than Lowly?
Yes! I am a little bit **fatter** than Lowly."

Lowly has been eating peas.
Peas are round in shape.

A ball is round, too.
But Lowly isn't able to eat that.

A block has a square shape.

An egg is oval-shaped.

The moon is sometimes crescent-shaped.

Oh, yes! Someone sent me a Valentine
in the shape of a heart.
Can you guess who sent it?

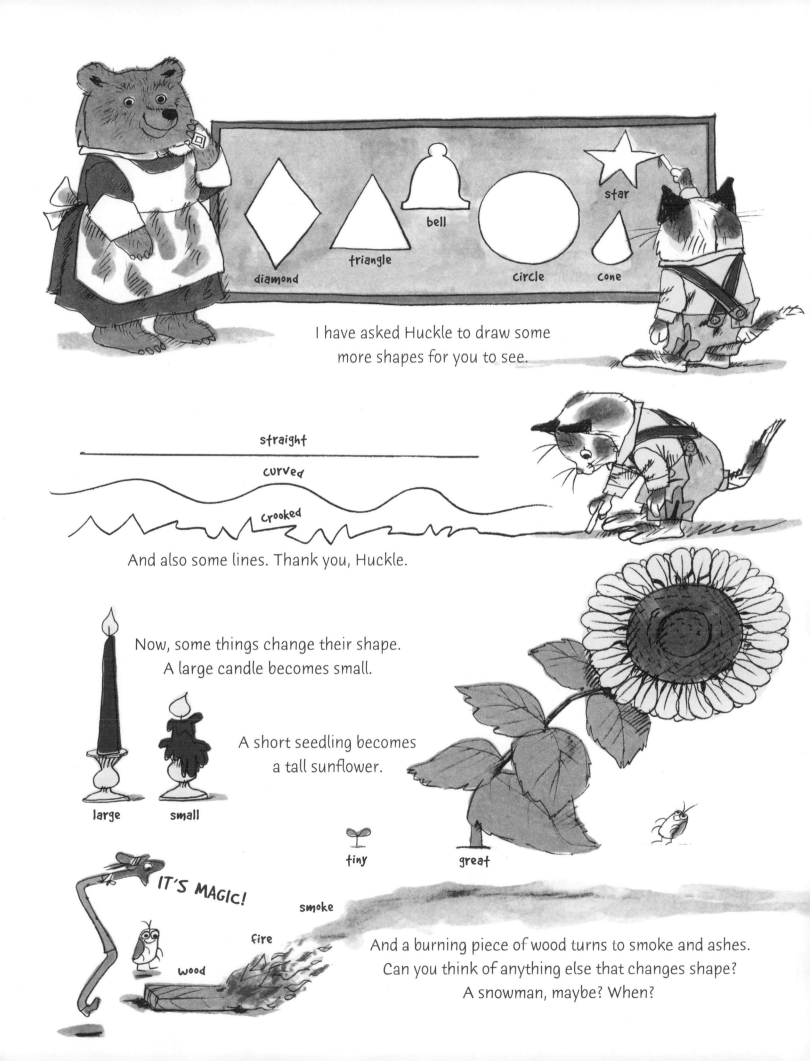

diamond

triangle

bell

circle

star

cone

I have asked Huckle to draw some
more shapes for you to see.

straight

curved

crooked

And also some lines. Thank you, Huckle.

Now, some things change their shape.
A large candle becomes small.

A short seedling becomes
a tall sunflower.

large

small

tiny

great

IT'S MAGIC!

smoke

fire

wood

And a burning piece of wood turns to smoke and ashes.
Can you think of anything else that changes shape?
A snowman, maybe? When?

Drawing and Painting

Drawing and painting are always fun. On drawing and painting days, Miss Honey's class is always full of artists. Some artists draw pictures with crayons or pencils. Some paint pictures with paint and water. All of them wear smocks so that they won't get their clothes messy.

Huckle helped the teacher pass out the drawing and painting materials.

These are some of the things he handed to the other artists.

pencils

pencil sharpener

sheets of paper

rubber

crayons

ball-point pen

marker pen

paint jars

pastels

water dish

mixing tray

paint brush

paint box

At last everyone was ready.

Mildred Hippo placed a pad of paper on her easel. She drew an insect with her pencil.

easel

Elizabeth Rabbit drew a picture with her pastels. She pinned it on the wall.

MY DOLL

Arthur Pig painted a red apple on the paper.

paint   water

picture

Bobby Cat painted some red footprints on the floor.

Roger Raccoon went to the sink to wash the dirty paint water out of his water dish. He ran the water too hard. He made a spatter painting.

sink

My! What a busy group of artists!

Colours

Huckle will show some of the things he has painted.

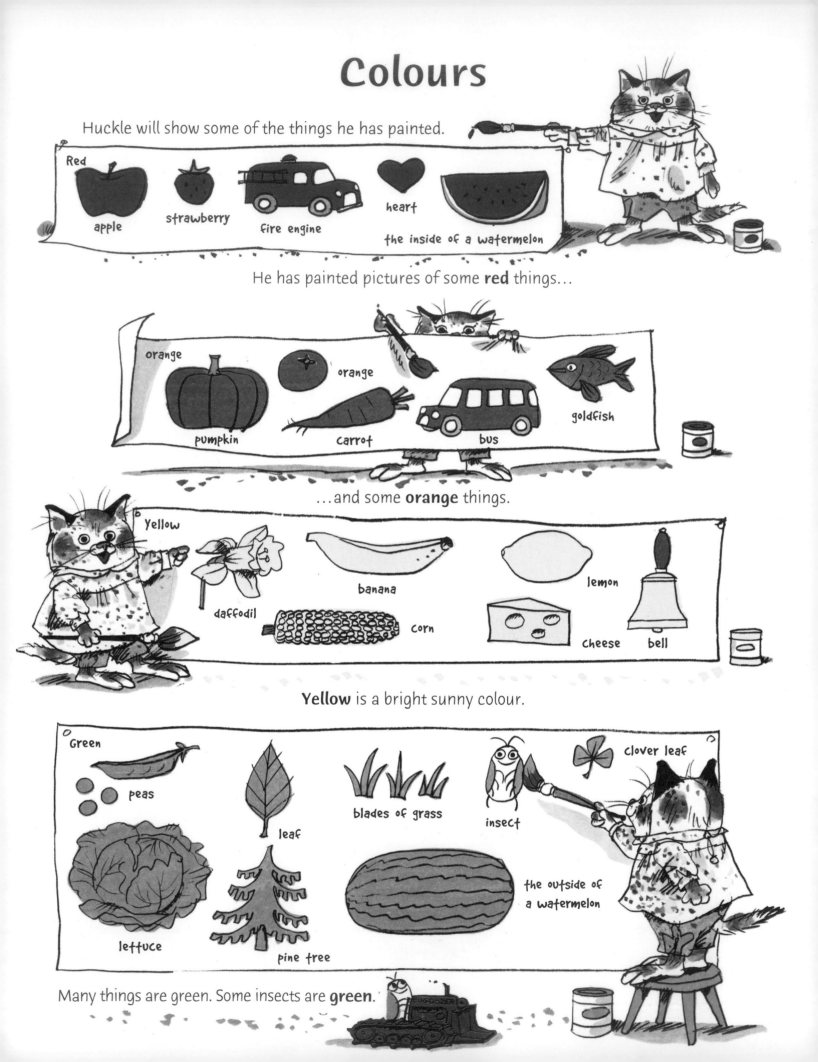

Red
- apple
- strawberry
- fire engine
- heart
- the inside of a watermelon

He has painted pictures of some **red** things…

- orange
- pumpkin
- orange
- carrot
- bus
- goldfish

…and some **orange** things.

Yellow
- daffodil
- banana
- corn
- lemon
- cheese
- bell

Yellow is a bright sunny colour.

Green
- peas
- leaf
- blades of grass
- insect
- clover leaf
- lettuce
- pine tree
- the outside of a watermelon

Many things are green. Some insects are **green**.

Blue

cloud sky

blueberries

bluebells

yacht

Huckle painted a **blue** sky.
When it is cloudy, the sky is
coloured grey. Be careful, Huckle

Violet or Purple

violet

plum

pansy

thistle

grapes

Huckle painted the floor **violet**.
Purple is almost the same colour as violet.

Brown

walnut

potato

chocolate
Easter Bunny

shoelace

light dark

Colours can be light or dark. A potato is **light brown**.
A chocolate Easter bunny is **dark brown**.

Black

doorbell

gumdrop

hat

tyre

White

egg

snowman

He painted some **black** things…   …and some white ones.

Besides painting pictures, Huckle painted himself.
Wash the paint off, Huckle, and put on a clean smock. Thank you!

Mixing Colours

Huckle will now show how to mix two colours together to make a third colour. Begin, Huckle!

worm

Red   →   orange   ←   Yellow

Red mixed with yellow makes orange.

frog

Yellow   →   Green   ←   Blue

Yellow and blue make green.

lizard

Red   →   Violet or Purple   ←   Blue

Red and blue make violet or purple.

snail

Red   →   Pink   ←   White

Red and white make pink.

fish

White   →   Grey   ←   Black

White and black make grey.

You are a fine colour mixer, Huckle. Now, will YOU be able to remember how to mix colours next time you paint? Of course you will!

Learning to Write
Learning to print

When the letters of the alphabet are written, they look different to letters that are printed. Written letters are connected to each other.

Miss Honey is going to teach her class how to write.
The first letter in your name is always a big capital letter.
The others are small letters.

This is how Albert's name looks printed: **Albert**

And this is how it looks written: *Albert*

A a / A a

Albert has an apple in his hand
Albert has an apple in his hand

B b / B b

Bananas Gorilla is being silly
Bananas Gorilla is being silly

C c / C c

Charlie Anteater is chewing gum
Charlie Anteater is chewing gum

That is very nice writing, boys!

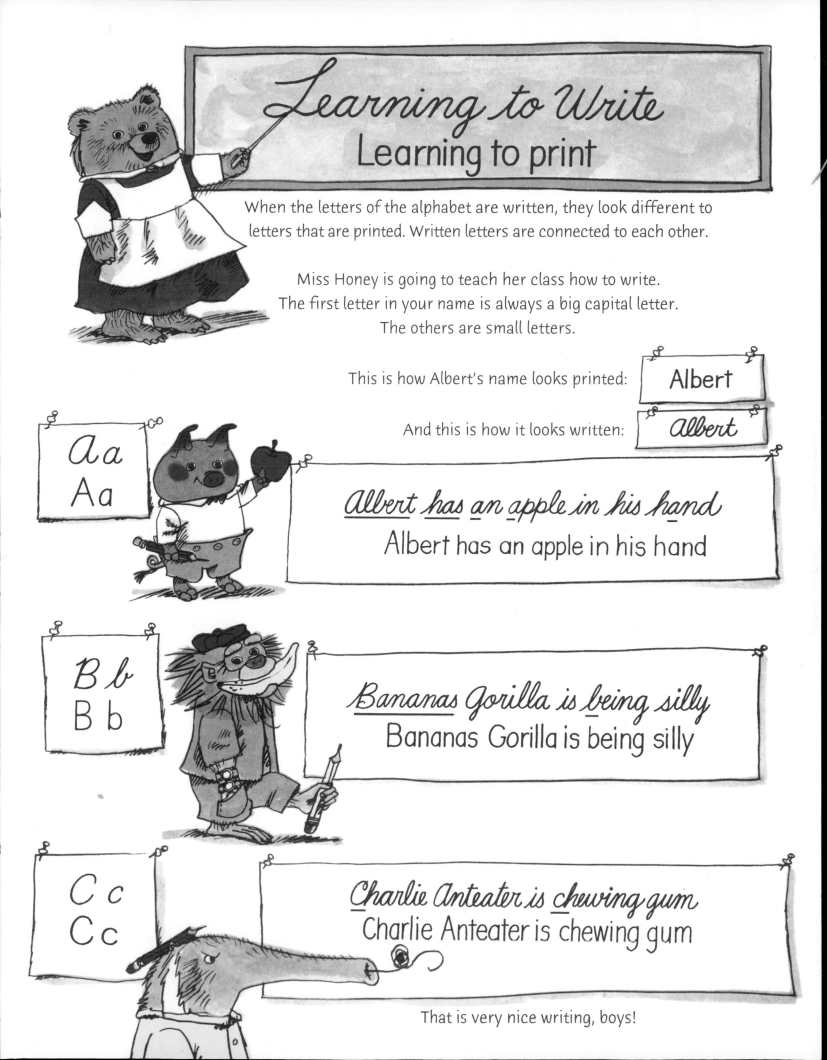

"Now, Huckle," said Miss Honey, "will you please write all the letters of the alphabet? I want all the children to copy them. With a little help, maybe they will be able to write their own names."

sharpen your pencil!

Aa Bb Cc Dd

Aa Bb Cc Dd

Ee Ff Gg Hh

Ee Ff Gg Hh

Ii Jj Kk Ll

Ii Jj Kk Ll

Mm Nn Oo Pp

Mm Nn Oo Pp

Qq Rr Ss Tt

Qq Rr Ss Tt

Uu Vv Ww Xx

Uu Vv Ww Xx

Yy Zz

Yy Zz

Now, everyone, please take a pencil and paper and try to write your own name.

Caretaker Joe and the Months of the Year

Joe is our school caretaker. A caretaker takes care of the schoolhouse. He fixes things when they get broken. He works around the school all twelve months of the year.

The first month of the year is **January**. January is a snowy month. When it snows, Joe shovels a path through the deep snow.

In **February**, he spreads sand on the icy pavement so that no one will slip.

What happened?
Did you slip, Joe?

ice

In **March**, the strong winds blow. Joe empties the wastepaper into the wire basket outside.

In **April** the rain falls from the sky and makes the plants grow.
Joe makes sure that the plants growing in the school flower garden get plenty of water.

The Easter Bunny comes in April

In **May** Joe mows the school lawn with his lawnmower.
Once the mower got away and ran into a supermarket.
Do you suppose it was tired of chewing
nothing but grass?

In **June** Miss Honey asked Joe to fix a table.
One leg wobbled a little bit.

Well, he really fixed that table, didn't he?
You can fix it correctly during our summer holidays.
We will see you in the autumn. Keep the school
looking nice, Joe!

In **July**, when everyone
was away on holiday,
Joe gave everything
a fresh coat of paint.

The month of **August** is very hot and sunny. That's when Joe fixed the showers in the gym. He pretended he was at the seashore.

In **September** school begins. Joe made a new cement pavement for the children to walk on. It is now soft and wet. Tomorrow it will be hard and dry. I think you should have made it a few days sooner, Joe!

nice work, Joe!

In **October**, the leaves begin to fall. Joe raked them up and carried them in his wheelbarrow to a big pile. He burned them in an open place so that nothing else would catch fire.

JOE! You left the wheelbarrow too close to the fire!

November is a cold and windy month. Winter is coming. Joe sawed the dead branches off the trees so that they wouldn't be broken off by the wind and fall on top of something. The head came out to look at his new car.

In **December** there are lots of holiday celebrations. Joe put up the school Christmas tree. He decorated it with ornaments. It looks beautiful. So far Joe has done something right. He only has to put the star on the top of the tree. Can you reach it, Joe?

The School Library

Now, where was Miss Honey taking the children?
She was taking them to the school library!
She was going to read stories to them
out of some library books.

The library shelves were full of all kinds of books.
Miss Honey gathered her children around and read some exciting stories.

She read a fairy tale about a pretty
princess and a brave knight.
The knight had a fight with a dragon.

She told them a story about a little boy who
lived in an igloo far away in the cold North.
An igloo is a house made of blocks of ice.

"Look at the picture of the boy
paddling his kayak in the
water," said Miss Honey.

When she finished reading, Miss Honey said, "Any child who
can write his or her name on a library card will be able
to take a book home to read!"

Miss Honey took a rubber stamp and stamped a date
in Huckle's book. Now he will know on what day he must
return the book to the library. The other children waited
their turn to borrow a book.

Huckle rode home
on the school bus. Mother Cat
was waiting for him.

Huckle showed her his library card. She was so pleased
to find that Huckle could write his own name!

"Huckle! You are really learning a lot in school!" she said.
Huckle hurried into the house to read his book.

Now, at least once every school year,
Miss Honey takes the children on a school picnic.
Mr Bruno was invited, too. He cooked the hot dogs.
Miss Honey poured the lemonade.

Bananas Gorilla played his Banana Guitar.
Huckle scooped out the ice cream.
Joe brought his kite and showed everyone how to fly it.
And a very good time was had by one and all!

FINISH LINE